Leif!
I hope you have
fun "hunting" the birds
down Main Street with your
Nana and Bopa and learn a
little along the way 😊 -Amy Becker 5/15/22

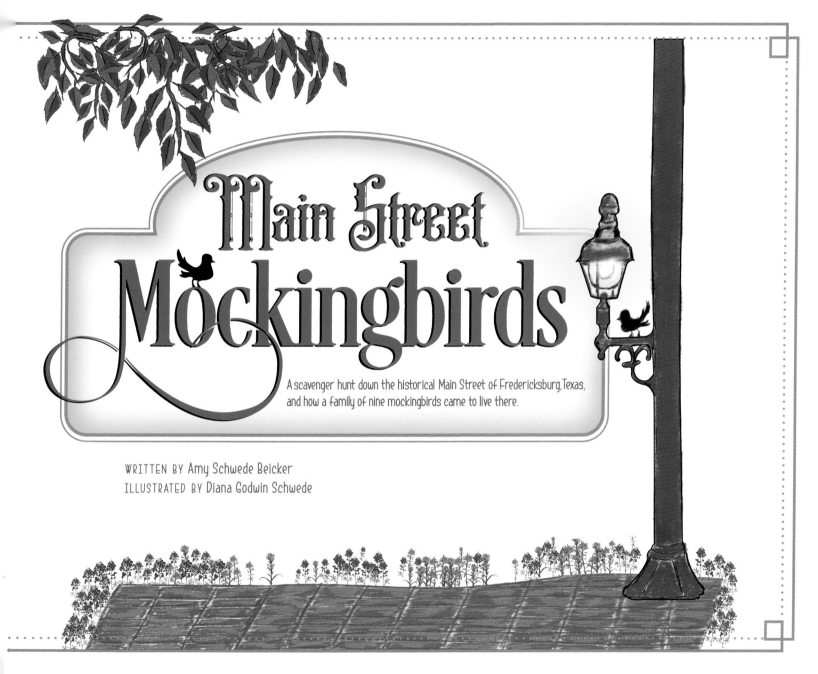

Main Street Mockingbirds

A scavenger hunt down the historical Main Street of Fredericksburg, Texas, and how a family of nine mockingbirds came to live there.

WRITTEN BY Amy Schwede Beicker

ILLUSTRATED BY Diana Godwin Schwede

Text Copyright 2018, 2021 by Amy Beicker
Illustrations Copyright 2020, 2021 by Diana Godwin Schwede

Beicker Publishing
412 S Adams, #1180
Fredericksburg, TX 78624
830-560-6361
amarierd@gmail.com

All royalties or profits from the sale of this book support Gillespie County Children's Foundation.

Library of Congress Control Number: 2021940218

Hardcover: 978-0-578-92417-5

10 9 8 7 6 5 4 3 2 1

Book Design by Brink Creative

Printed in Canada

Beyond the Main Street store fronts and old limestone facades,

These buildings tell a deeper tale that started far abroad.

It's hidden right in front of you, but also in plain sight.

If it was a rattle snake, you'd end up with a bite!

Old talking walls and riddled streets speak of how it came to be;

At least that's what these little birds once told me.

𝕾𝖎𝖑𝖑𝖐𝖔𝖒𝖒𝖊𝖓 to every pioneer that tries to discover,

All the treasures that are hinted at within this book's cover.

ALL WELCOME who seek and search;

COME BACK, 𝖆𝖚𝖋 𝖂𝖎𝖊𝖉𝖊𝖗𝖘𝖊𝖍𝖊𝖓 to those who find the mockingbirds' perch.

The city streets have their own hidden message!
Starting at the courthouse and heading east towards Austin, the streets spell out
ALL WELCOME (Adams, **L**lano, **L**incoln, **W**ashington, **E**lk, **L**ee, **C**olumbus, **O**live, **M**esquite,
and **E**agle**).** *Going west towards Mason from the courthouse the streets spell*
COME BACK (Crockett, **O**range, **M**ilam, **E**dison, **B**owie, **A**corn, **C**herry, *and* **K**ay**).**

Change was in the air as **Silver Wing** and **Willow**
landed in the large oak tree where their seven hatchlings
waited eagerly for their return.

𝕿𝖍𝖊 *nomadic Comanche*
Penateka, or "honey-eaters,"
inhabited the area, hunted buffalo,
and were excellent horseman.

"What did you see today, **Mama?** Did you bring anything back, **Papa?**"

"Were the Comanches hunting?" **Scout** asked.

"Want to bet if the bears caught any fish?" Challenged **Ace.**

"Did you find any berries to save for winter?" Questioned **Buck.**

"Or dried grass and sap to fix that hole in the nest?" Added **Fiddle.**

"Did the cicadas play a new song?" Piped in **Marriette.**

"Did you invite anyone over?" **Ranger** interrupted.

"Is the armadillo okay after rolling down the hill?" **Albertina** inquired.

"What about the wildflowers? Are they blooming? Yes! Tell us about the wildflowers!" They all chimed in.

Texas designated the mockingbird (Mimus polyglottos) as the official state bird in 1927 (Senate Concurrent Resolution No. 8) noting that, "it is found in all parts of the state...is a singer of distinctive type, a fighter for the protection of his home, falling, if need be in its defense, like any true Texan..." (Source: State Symbols: State Library Archives; State Symbols: Texas Legislature Online).

It was the spring of 1846 in the Texas Hill Country, and
the wildflowers were indeed in full bloom, but amongst
the blankets of blue and red, **Silver Wing** and **Willow**
had seen an odd group of people heading their way.
As the birds pondered their peculiarity, their silence only
heightened the hatchlings' curiosity, and their eyes grew big
with anticipation.

"Well," **Silver Wing** broke the silence, "new people are
coming from the east that are nothing like the Comanches.
They travel in covered wagons, wear different clothes, and
speak a different language. I don't know if they will stay;
they have so little. From the safety of our nest we will watch
and see."

It took 16 days by wagon for the
120 German immigrants
to make the 80 mile trip from
New Braunfels to their new home.

And watch they did as the new settlers nestled into the surrounding land and called it FRIEDRICHSBURG. As the town flourished, the tiny birds grew. The fair and just **Silver Wing** kept the birds in line with the rules, while **Willow** kept them calm and entertained with her stories. Soon, it was time for each mockingbird to find his own favorite place to perch.

 ❸

 **Friedrichsburg** *was named for Prince Frederick of Prussia, a member of the Adelsverein, the German society formed to establish a new Germany in Texas.*

One day as **Scout** soared over the river, he spotted several fires burning on the highest hills, but none of the settlers or Comanches were afraid. He landed on some nearby rocks as the Comanche chiefs shared a peace pipe and shook hands with Baron Meusebach, the leader of the settlers. **Scout** followed the two groups as they camped together and returned to a festive crowd in the heart of town.

4

The treaty was made between Meusebach, who was called "El Sol Colorado" for his long, flaring red beard, and the powerful chiefs, Buffalo Hump, Santa Anna, and Old Owl.

Meusebach began negotiations by emptying his firearms, showing the Chiefs he meant no harm. His attitude of equality and respect towards the Comanches set the stage for the peaceful years to follow between the Penteka and German settlers.

Legend has it that the Comanches used bonfires on the surrounding hills to communicate during the treaty negotiations. Left vulnerable and to speculate on the meanings of these bonfires, a German mother comforted her children by telling them it was the Easter bunny boiling water to color Easter eggs with wildflowers. Periodically, the town still re-enacts the signing of the treaty and the Easter fires with a pageant on Easter Eve.

The Vereins Kirche "Society
Church", was nicknamed the
Kaffeemühle (coffee mill) for
its octagonal shape.

From that day forward, the town grew more rapidly.
A little octagon-shaped building became the center
of much activity. It served as a schoolhouse, a church,
a town hall, and a fortress. Its bell chimes rang for miles
calling all to gather or to warn of an impending threat.

When the Peace Treaty's ceremonial signing was
held there, Scout proudly stood guard and kept
his post as secure as the treaty that went on to become
the longest known treaty kept between the Indians and
the settlers.

6

Scout's fun-loving brother, **Ace** hung around the WHITE ELEPHANT SALOON enjoying its card games, rowdy crowds, and late nights. He might not have understood why the carved elephant on the building symbolized German drinking halls, but he was quick and clever, and knew a good poker hand when he saw one. He was always ready to bet the nest but never allowed in the upper-back room where the stakes were much too high for a mockingbird.

The White Elephant was the most popular name for a saloon in 19th century Texas. There were White Elephants in Abilene, Austin, Brownsville, Brenham, Bryan, Denison, El Paso, Ft Worth, Lampasas, Laredo, Mobeetie, San Antonio, and Wichita Falls. The name was so familiar to Texas, it could have been a franchise.

In 1888 stone mason, A.W. Petmecky, borrowed a wooden elephant from a merry-go-round operator at a visiting carnival and pressed it into moist sand to make the elephant used on the front of the building.

A white elephant was a symbol for eating and drinking establishments in Germany thought to have its origins with a white pygmy elephant that was said to have been a pet of Hannibal when he set out to cross the Alps with 60,000 foot soldiers, 9000 horses, and some elephants.

Believing that a bird in the hand was worth more than two in the bush, **Buck** did not approve of **Ace's** late nights and risky betting. He liked the thrifty, hard-working German character of his new neighbors. When the BANK OF FREDERICKSBURG opened, Buck woke up early to get the worm and flew over to ask the banker to store his seed savings. It was the foggiest of mornings, but the bank's red-capped cupola made it easy to find. After the bank agreed to invest his nest egg, he became a frequent spectator at all the board meetings.

⑤

This building was the second location for the bank and was designed by **Alfred Giles**, *the same architect for the old court house. Do you see any similarities in their design?*

Architectural details and embellishments are a small part of the whole that add character and authenticity to their greater structure. Can you find some of the **unique design elements** *included on this particular building which has operated as a general store, a gift shop, an antique vendor, and an art gallery?*

Their skilled sister, **Fiddle,** had little time to worry with a nice perch. She was quite innovative and stayed busy gathering materials to make repairs or to complete her latest invention. That is until one of the Itz sons, August, opened his general store in 1908. The Itz family lived upstairs and ran their business downstairs where **Fiddle** could often be found rummaging through the inventory.

The store became a bustle on weekends when rural families came to town to trade goods and attend church. The families would stop at the store for their weekly necessities before spending the night in town at their Sunday houses. The regular customers kept **Fiddle** in tune with the town gossip, while she fluttered around collecting materials for her next project.

Marriette on the other hand enjoyed the coziness of one of these Sunday houses. When the settlers had arrived, they received a town lot and 10 acres in the country. Many families, like the Webers, opted to build a Sunday house in town for weekends, but lived on their farm.

The Weber's vacant little house served as a sweet spot for the timid **Marriette** to practice her lovely harmonizing tweets. When the weekend came around, she savored the comforting aroma of a Sunday roast stewing while she sang a background tune and the Webers relaxed on the porch.

Apart *from a short revival during the gas rationing of World War II, Sunday houses fell out of use with the invention of the automobile that made same-day trips possible for farmers.*

8

Charles Nimitz *was not only a hotel owner and the grandfather and role model for Fleet Admiral Chester Nimitz, but also a German sea captain, a Texas Ranger, a Confederate officer, a cook at Ft. Martin Scott, and a state representative.*

All the mockingbirds enjoyed the chatter of the newcomers and those passing through, but **Ranger** especially enjoyed perching next to the new hotel where the brave seaman, Charles Nimitz, offered weary guests a good night's rest and a cold drink.

As one of the last hotels on the long stagecoach trail from Texas to California, it maintained a steady flow of all kinds of interesting characters. From Presidents Rutherford B. Hayes and Ulysses S. Grant to General Robert E. Lee and outlaw Johnny Ringo, there was always a conversation worth listening to at the NIMITZ HOTEL.

Nimitz *added the famous steamboat shaped exterior sometime after 1888.*

But everything did not come easy on the frontier. **Albertina** watched with a heavy heart as the settlers and Comanches struggled to survive tough conditions and diseases. Her chirping became more hopeful when the first doctor arrived. She admired how Dr. Wilhelm Keidel cared for the Comanches and settlers alike and tended to both Union and Confederate soldiers during the Civil War. He never had a hospital to work in, but **Albertina** delighted in flying over the town and perching where she could find the kind doctor at work.

Years later, when Dr. Keidel's grandson founded the KEIDEL MEMORIAL HOSPITAL AND CLINIC, **Albertina** landed close by tweeting a comforting tune as the patients recovered inside.

Native tribes paid Dr. Keidel by hanging fresh venison or turkeys in nearby trees.

Dr. Keidel's wife, Albertina, died in childbirth of their son, Albert Keidel. Albert and his son Victor, both became physicians and contributed to the building that eventually became The Keidel Memorial Hospital and Clinic in 1938.

With no fledglings left in their nest, **Silver Wing** and **Willow** left the old oak tree. The empty nesters made a home where **Silver Wing** continued to be a fair judge, settling disputes and offering prudent guidance to his offspring, while **Willow** enjoyed reading them stories as often as they would visit.

3

The first courthouse no longer stands, but the second one designed by 𝔄𝔩𝔣𝔯𝔢𝔡 𝔊𝔦𝔩𝔢𝔰, *served the county from 1882 to 1939 and is now the home to the Pioneer Memorial Library.*

From their new nest **Silver Wing** and **Willow** looked down MAIN STREET at their little birds, reminiscing about how they, much like the settlers living alongside them, had come to perch right where they were always meant to be.

Das Ende

Fredericksburg's [𝕸aibaum], or Maypole, is another landmark commemorating the history of our town. Now that the mockingbirds have told their tale, can you find the Maypole and recognize some of the history it portrays?

CONTRIBUTORS

Amy Schwede Beicker, *Author* lives in Fredericksburg with her husband, Clint, and is the proud mom of three kids. Although always an eager learner, it was not until exploring the world through her children's eyes that her delight in the hidden treasures around her really took off. She hopes this project not only brings history to life, but gets families outside to explore the world together, creating memories that make Fredericskburg's story their own. She is grateful for this opportunity to pursue a dream and for all the talented people who made it possible. She dedicates this work to Mom and Dad who taught her that history and faith matter; to Bliss, Bowen, and Brooke who opened her eyes to the joy of the present; and to Clint, who encouraged her every step of the way.

Diana Godwin Schwede, *Illustrator* has raised three daughters with her husband, Gary. They now have nine grandchildren. She loves design, British history and literature. She is fiercely committed to using her talents to create adventures for her family, be it by creating a family-friendly hill country retreat in Mason, transforming the family homestead into a beautiful B&B, or illustrating her daughter's first book. Diana's hope is that her illustrations bring life and color to Amy's story; motivating children of all ages to explore the history that surrounds them. She feels blessed beyond measure having this unique opportunity to partner with Amy on this project.

John Bennett, *Sculptor* has lived in Fredericksburg since 2006 with his wife Cathy. He has been sculpting since 1976 and was designated Texas State Artist by the 81st Texas Legislature in 2010. Commissions include bronze sculptures for the Perry and Ruby Stephens Charitable Foundation in Kerrville and lifesize bronzes of Annie Oakley and Alice Reeves (former school teacher and granddaughter of a slave) for the Leesburg Public Library in Leesburg, Florida. Purchasers include the National Cowgirl Museum and Hall of Fame in Ft. Worth and the Women's Museum in Dallas. His work was displayed at the White House in 1999 as part of the federal 'Save America's Treasures' project. John works from his studio in Fredericksburg and is represented by Gallery 330 on Main Street.

Jennifer Braham, *Book Designer* lives on her farm in a small rural town in central Texas. Here, she enjoys toggling between her passions of designing logos, websites, books and collateral while she is also building an off the grid home. All of these processes bring together liked minded, passionate and fun people. Jennifer enjoys this community building and she is always delighted by the surprising beautiful outcomes of the collaborative hard work. This book is the perfect example of such a satisfying process. Jennifer's dozens of chickens, many dogs, cats and ducks keep her laughing on a daily basis. Brink Creative, her design business of 25 years, sustains her on every level, as she works with people who are shifting the perception of our culture. Her many tropical plants remind her that life (with its ebbs and flows) is ever bountiful.

SPECIAL THANKS TO

Dian Graves Owen Foundation

Texas Hill Country Orthopaedics & Sports Medicine

HEB

and the charitable local families for their generous donations
and to the Fredericksburg City Council for allocating tourism funds to the publication of
this book and production of the accompanying sculptures. Without their combined support,
this project would not have been brought to our community.

Unless otherwise noted, historical images and information courtesy of
the Gillespie County Historical Society in Fredericksburg, Texas.
Visit them at 325 W Main Street or give them a call (830) 990-8441.
To learn more go to   pioneermuseum.org

For more information on Fredericksburg's happenings and attractions,
visit the Fredericksburg Convention & Visitor Bureau at 302 E Austin Street
or give them a call at (830) 997-6523.
For their local lodging suggestions visit their lodging website
at www.visitfredericksburgtx.com/lodging/

Main Street Mockingbirds
Map & Key

1 Marriette

8 Ranger

2 Fiddle

7 Albertina

3 Silver Wing

&

3 Willow

1 Scout

5 Buck

6 Ace

N.Milam · N.Orange · N.Crockett · N.Adams · N.Llano · N.Lincoln · N.Washington

◄ TO MASON

Main Street

TO AUSTIN ►

S.Milam · S.Orange · N.Crockett · S.Adams · S.Llano · S.Lincoln · S.Washington